ISBN-13: 978-1-56383-630-5
Item #4103

**Printed in the USA
by G&R Publishing Co.**

Distributed By:

507 Industrial Street
Waverly, IA 50677

www.cqbookstore.com

gifts@cqbookstore.com

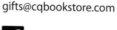 CQ Products

 CQ Products

 @cqproducts

 @cqproducts

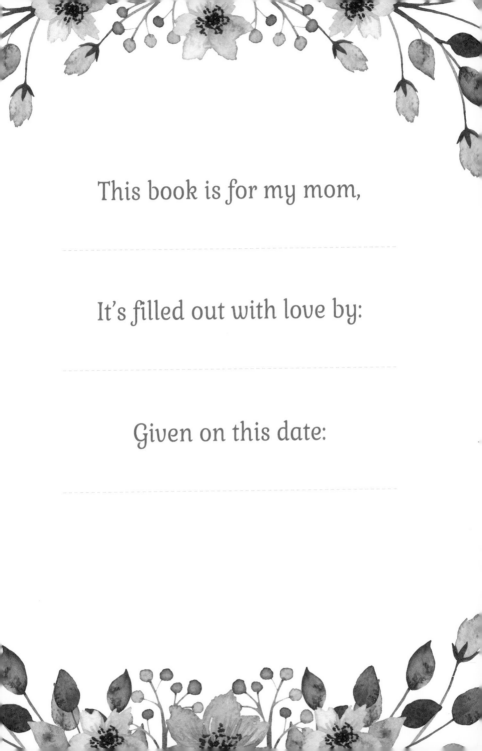

This book is for my mom,

It's filled out with love by:

Given on this date:

One of my first memories of you...

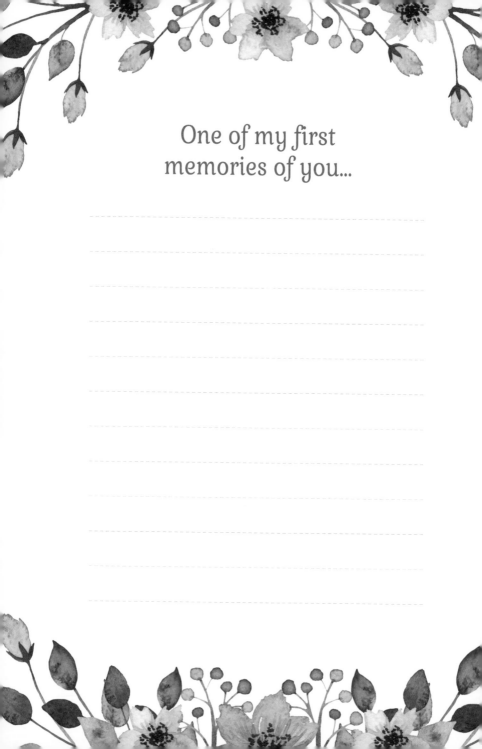

When I think about our house growing up...

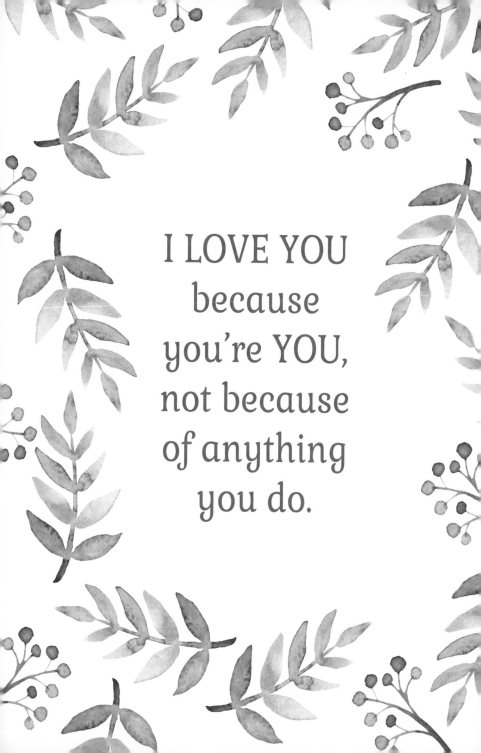

I LOVE YOU
because
you're YOU,
not because
of anything
you do.

My favorite meal growing up...

...I can almost smell it!

I miss this most about
being a kid...

When I think about a typical
day at home when I
was young, you were...

The place my heart will
always call home is...

Your home now makes
me think about...

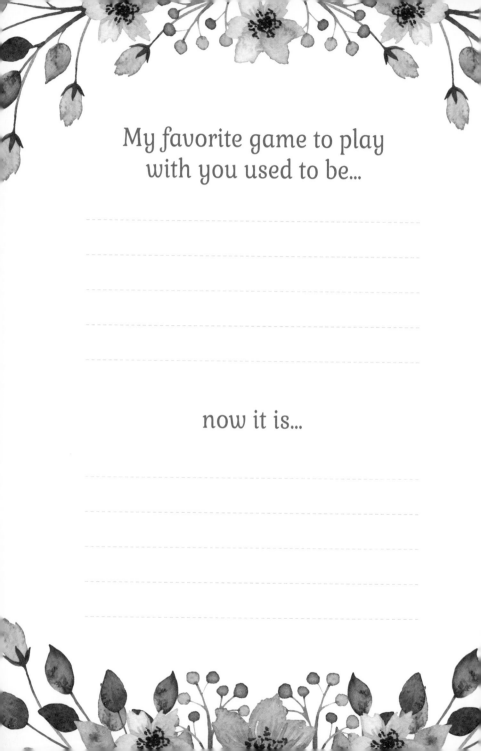

My favorite game to play with you used to be...

now it is...

Growing up, spending time
with you meant...

_____

_____

_____

_____

The time we spend
together now...

_____

_____

_____

_____

Our shared adventures...

(Shade where you've visited together and
notate where you've lived together.)

Others:

My favorite places
we visited are...

because...

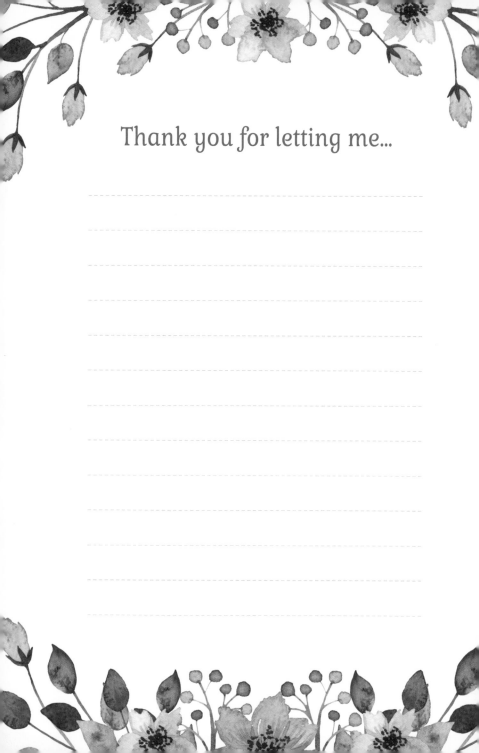

Thank you for letting me...

I know I tested your patience when...

Speaking of patience, remember the time...

Remember how we always
used to fight about...

---

but we always laughed about...

Remember that time you grounded me for...

I definitely did / did not deserve it!
(choose)

You used to always tell me to...

----

and I finally understand...

To the world
you are a
mother,
but to your
family
you are the
WORLD!

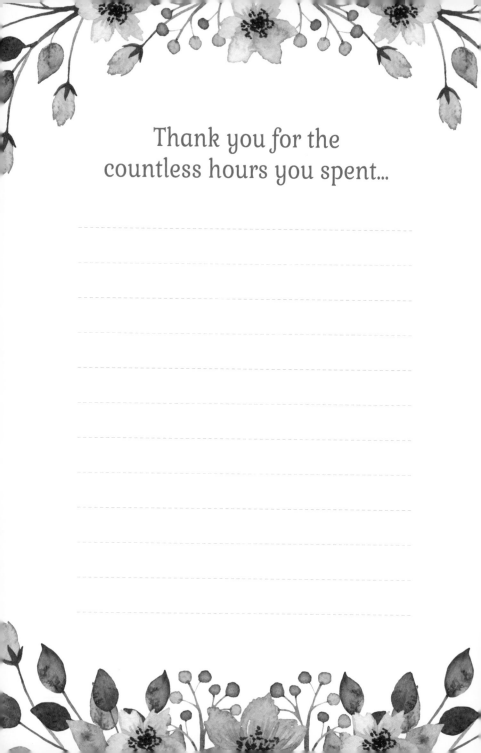

Thank you for the
countless hours you spent...

You taught me the
importance of...

a Mother's
hug lasts
long after she
lets go

I always loved hanging
out with you...

because...

Some things you and I enjoyed doing together...

One of my outfits that I loved
and you hated was...

Your response to it was...

Although I complained at the time, thank you for making me do these chores...

I secretly enjoyed this chore...

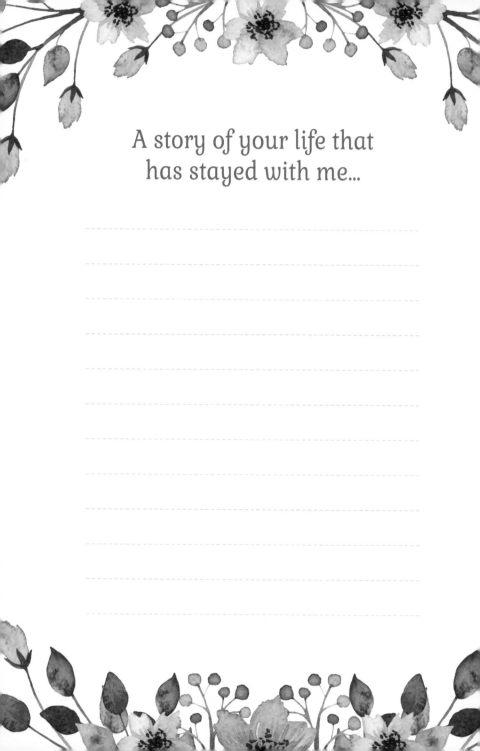

A story of your life that has stayed with me...

A song that always reminds me of you is...

because...

You encouraged me to...

If it wasn't for you, I never
would have...

Thank you for putting
up with me when I...

_____

_____

_____

_____

I was always so happy
when you...

_____

_____

_____

_____

What we enjoy: (circle choice)

Me

comedy or drama

city or country

beach or mountains

tea or coffee

TV or radio

sweet or salty

morning or evening

dog or cat

movies or books

spring or fall

cake or pie

You

comedy or drama

city or country

beach or mountains

tea or coffee

TV or radio

sweet or salty

morning or evening

dog or cat

movies or books

spring or fall

cake or pie

Things I say now that remind me of you...

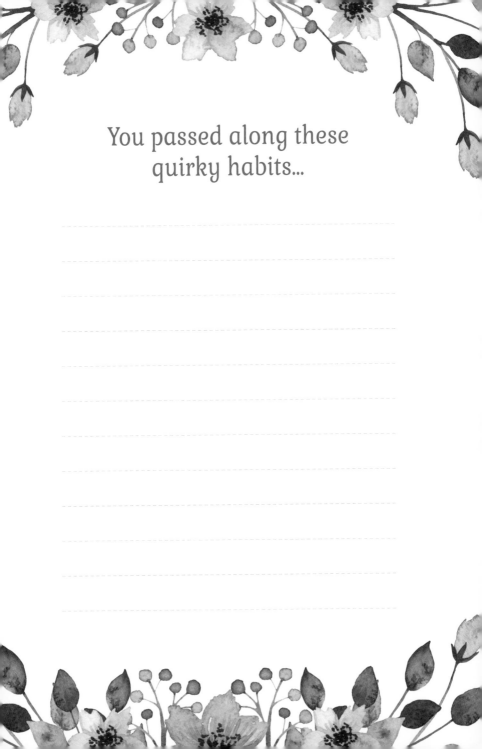

You passed along these quirky habits...

One of my biggest fears
as a child was...

This is how you helped
me with it...

Long car rides for our family usually involved...

_____

_____

_____

_____

Motherhood–
the scariest
Hood
you'll ever
go through

Moms
You Are
The
Best

Your laugh makes me...

I laugh whenever I think about...

FAMILY
Like branches
on a tree,
we all grow
in different
directions,
yet our roots
remain as one.

I love to tease you about...

But to be fair, you always
tease me about...

Some of the traits I admire most about you...

I'm beginning to see
more of you in me...

I've inherited your...

Something you tried to teach
me that didn't go so well...

Our greatest
accomplishment together...

One thing you said or did that means the world to me...

_____

_____

_____

_____

Sometimes the smallest things take up the most room in your Heart

Winnie the Pooh

You're my go-to expert on...

Something I still wish
you would teach me...

Your hidden talents are...

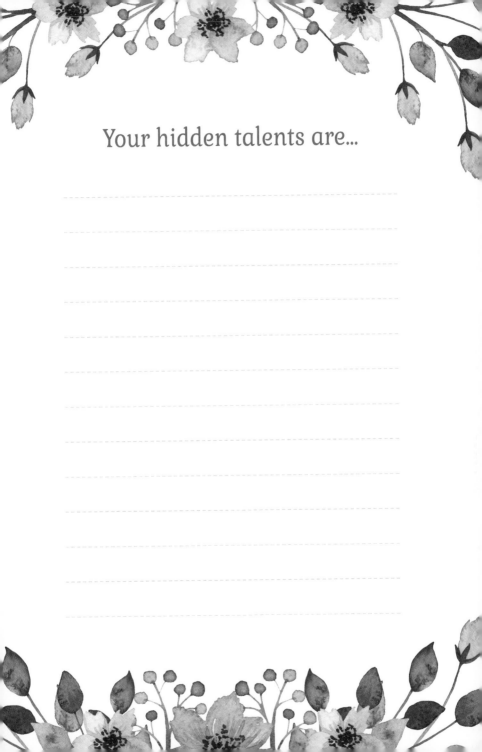

Life doesn't come with a manual, it comes with a MOTHER!

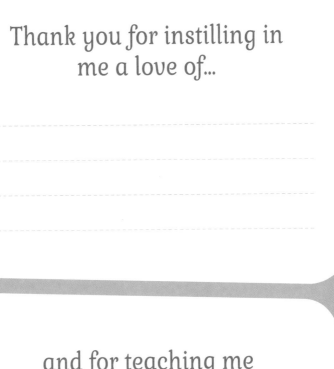

Thank you for instilling in
me a love of...

_____

_____

_____

_____

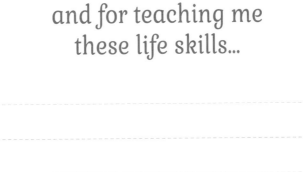

and for teaching me
these life skills...

_____

_____

_____

_____

If you had a superpower, it would be...

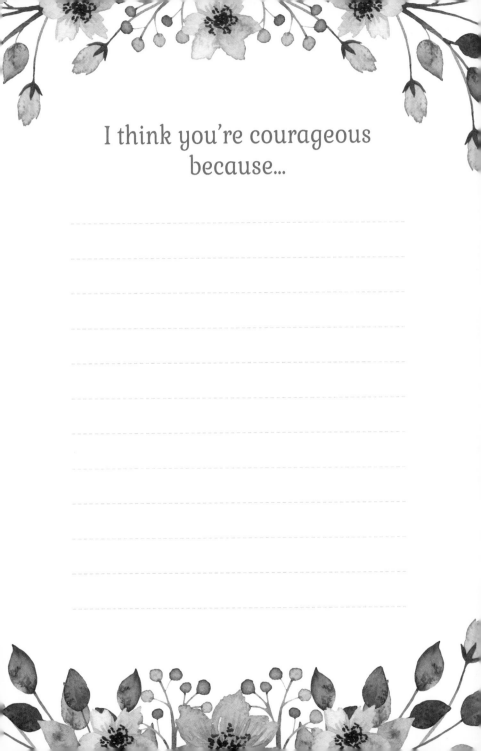

I think you're courageous because...

I love that we have
the same taste in...

_____

_____

_____

_____

_____

but we disagree on this...

_____

_____

_____

_____

_____

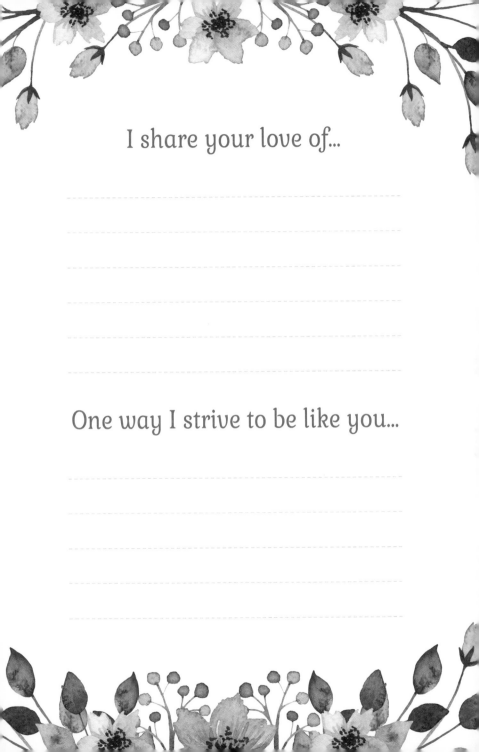

I share your love of...

One way I strive to be like you...

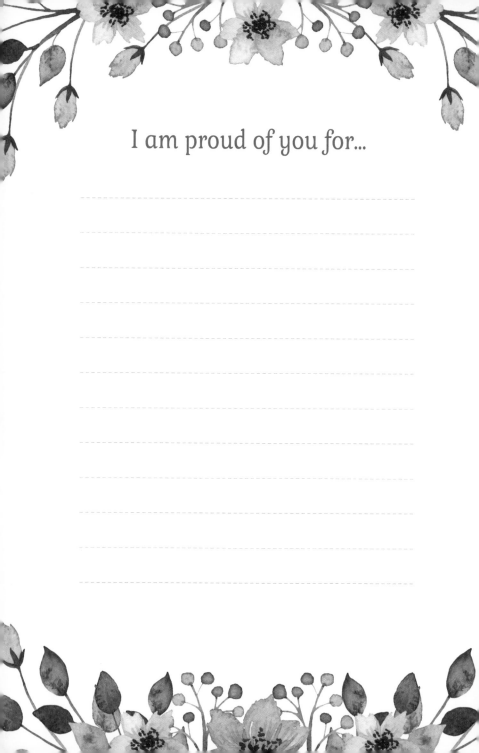

I am proud of you for...

The world is a better place
because of your...

_____

_____

_____

_____

all that I am
or Hope to be
I owe to
my Mother

Abraham Lincoln

These are my favorite family traditions...

If I could give you any gift, it would be...

Some of the
absolute
BEST THINGS
in life are
silly and
unnecessary.

One of the silliest things I
remember you doing...

One of the most unnecessary
things I remember
you doing for me...

As I navigate my life,
I'm thankful that you...

I love that you love my...

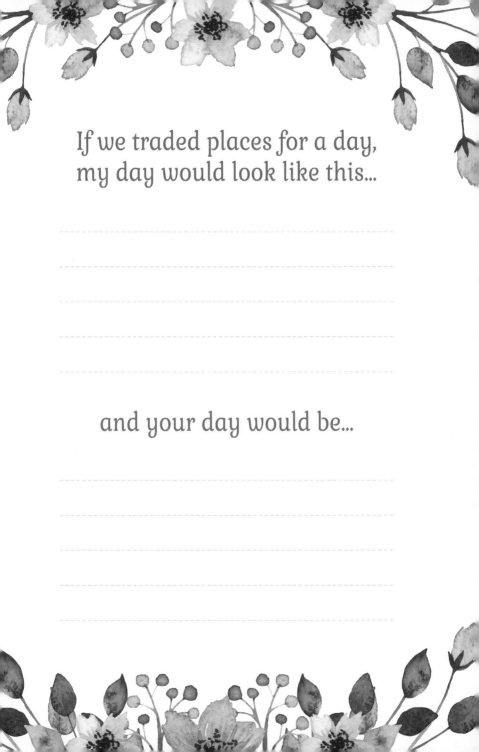

If we traded places for a day,
my day would look like this...

and your day would be...

I will cherish these memories forever...

Vacation:

Summer:

Holidays:

Birthdays:

It's the
little memories
that will
last a
LIFETIME

These are favorites that we have shared...

movie or TV show:

restaurant:

hobby:

guilty pleasure:

meal:

holiday:

This is my favorite photo of us.

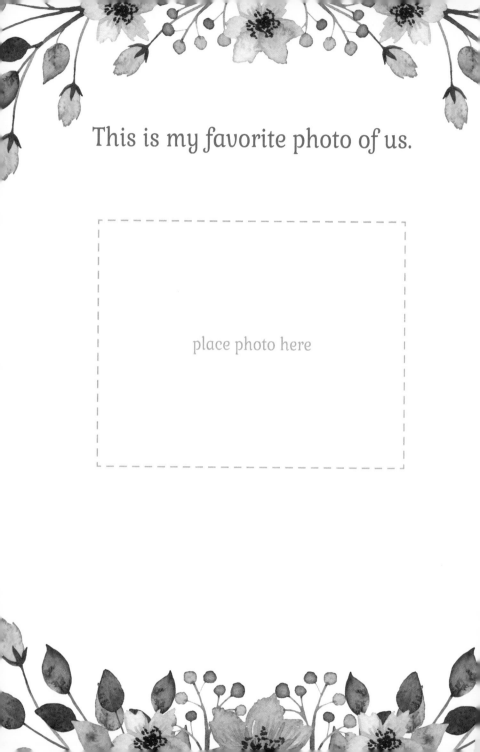

place photo here